Life On
Earth
Coloring
Books

let art
photographers
Life On
Earth
Coloring
Books
inspire you

Disclaimer

All excerpts from this book are solely intended to provide an instructive component to Michael Peter's artwork. Note that all texts are mainly based on architectural or historical facts, for informational purposes only; the choice of texts was made excluding as much as possible any political or religious point of view. Although every effort has been made to ensure the links provided to external websites are accurate, up to date and relevant, we cannot take responsibility for pages maintained by external providers.

"Creativity is intelligence having fun."

(Albert Einstein)

Life On Earth is a project that took shape unexpectedly in 2017. It has given me and my family the same desire to meet the challenge of a common goal. The objectives that we have achieved together over time have been self-fulfilling and exciting. Besides, reaching goals and carrying out projects improves well-being.

Everyone needs a project. We wanted to bring you just that.

The Benefits of Coloring

Ideal for all ages and abilities, coloring is more than just an enjoyable past time. In fact, since 2014, it has received praise from various sources around the world like CNN, Fox News, Huffington Post, Washington Post, Publishers Weekly, Independent, Dailymail, The Star, NY Daily News, Smithsonian Magazine, The Guardian, ABC (Australia), The Sydney Morning Herald, China Daily, Times of India, Vogue, Business Insider, Economist, Wall Street Journal, Mashable, Entrepreneur, New York Post, The Telegraph, CBC, The Globe and Mail and Global News.

Coloring is a fascinating activity that helps promote good motor skills, develop concentration and prove to be of benefit.[1] People who are recuperating from illness or dealing with a difficult time in their lives find coloring to be relaxing and to have an almost meditative effect. Back in the early 1900s, Carl Jung used coloring as a relaxation technique.[2] Just like meditation, coloring also allows us to switch off our brains from other thoughts and focus only on the moment. Making art can significantly reduce stress-related hormones in your body.[3]

The process of shading, blending, selecting various hues and adding your own touches do challenge one's artistic side. But coloring still works even if you believe you lack artistic skills. Let your imagination runs riot as you color in and experience the joys and challenges of creation.

1   Fitzpatrick, Kelly. "Why Adult Coloring Books are Good for You." *CNN*, 1 August 2017, www.cnn.com/2016/01/06/health/adult-coloring-books-popularity-mental-health/index.html. Accessed 15 March 2020.

2   Jones, Orion. "How Adult Coloring Books Can Bring Out The Artist in You." *Big Think*, 16 October 2015, bigthink.com/ideafeed/how-adult-coloring-books-can-bring-out-the-artist-in-you. Accessed 15 March 2020.

3   Taylor, Jordyn. "The Science Behind Adult Coloring Books Explains Why There're So Therapeutic." *MIC*, 16 June 2016, www.mic.com/articles/146396/the-science-behind-adult-coloring-books-explains-why-they-re-so-therapeutic. Accessed 15 March 2020.

Fine Art Photography

Unlike any other visual image, a photograph is not a rendering, an imitation or an interpretation of its subject, but actually a trace of it.[1]

The sort of photography viewed as art is the kind of work that reflects a thought process and in which both technical and artistic skills are evident. If art implies control of reality,[2] photography becomes art when certain controls are applied; it is the art of real life – however manipulated. The photography that meets the criteria of the art world is just a tiny sliver of the camera's artistic riches. It is not about capturing what the camera sees; it is about capturing what the artist sees.

Photographic image is the successor to the great art of the past. It also happens to be the most accessible and democratic way of making art that has ever been invented. The greatness of art lies in human insight.[3]

Institutions who are most supportive of photographic art include the Art Institute of Chicago, the Metropolitan and the Museum of Modern Art of New York and the Aperture Foundation.[4]

1   Plumridge, Jo. "Is Photography an Art Form?" *Contrastly*, 24 February 2014, contrastly.com/photography-art-form/. Accessed 15 March 2020.

2   Rivera-Uncapher, Brian. "What is Fine Art Photography?" *Photography Life*, last updated 18 February 2019, photographylife.com/what-is-fine-art-photography. Accessed 15 March 2020.

3   Jones, Jonathan. "Photography is the Art of Our Time." *The Guardian*, 10 January 2013, www.theguardian.com/artanddesign/jonathanjonesblog/2013/jan/10/photography-art-of-our-time. Accessed 15 March 2020.

4   "Fine Art Photography, Definition, History, Types - Galleries." *Encyclopedia of Art Education, visual-arts-cork.com*, 2 May 2012, www.visual-arts-cork.com/fine-art-photography.htm. Accessed 15 March 2020.

Life On Earth, the Collection

This collection of coloring books is the first of its kind as it is created by professional photographers. Exclusive to each series, the compiled selection of photographs highlights iconic sites, places, aspects and golden moments in life you will enjoy discovering. Each book shows you the world through the photographer's eyes and reflects the artist's unique perspective.

Moreover, this collection reveals the art of coloring in a new light by the juxtaposition of the original photograph and its drawing, as the sketch method developed therein accurately depicts striking details for you to explore. Not to mention that all the drawings are produced by the artist.

As the colorist, you will feel invited to take it up a notch by blending colors, adding shadings and honing your creative skills. Fresh and engaging, you will notice this side-by-side presentation promotes your analysis of the challenge at a glance. The leading illustration therefore offers a guideline that you may find appealing.

This exceptional artwork will challenge the most dedicated coloring book enthusiasts whether or not you choose to follow the original photograph. Pick your preferred tools to color in 24 drawings from the fine art photographer, Michael Peter.

The Artist and His Artwork

With the rise of social networks, our modern and very visual world reveals the nature of our bonds as we have become even more acutely aware of photographs and the perspective of the vulnerability of existence. Photography is indeed the art of real life.

Our contact with reality depends on the hypothesis we adopt about what is truth and what is illusion specially if we consider, on the one hand, an orchestrated and beautified environment and, on the other hand, raw materials from which the history is made. Hence, the landscape creates a view depending on where we stand and takes into account the idea that any view implies a given point that interacts with history, memory and time.

Michael Peter seeks to glorify the image and its lines and at the same time to reflect the steps of urban history, revisiting it from a formal point of view.

He finds inspiration in architectural wonders and reveals the urban aesthetic. With his artworks that portray intelligently the visions and limits of our society, its history and its development, unobtrusively he mixes contemporary representations of architectural lines with those historical and almost invisible paths laid by the past.

In this timeless series, Michael Peter takes you on his journey through Manhattan.

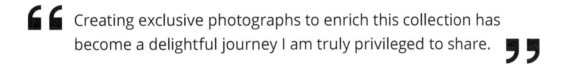

> " Creating exclusive photographs to enrich this collection has become a delightful journey I am truly privileged to share. "

Manhattan

Pronunciation: \ Manaháhtaan \

Definition: the place for gathering the wood to make bows

Hence, it is from an ancient culture that relied on a deep knowledge of the environment and available resources that the origin of the Manhattan comes from.[1]

1   Goddard, Ives. "The Origin and Meaning of the Name 'Manhattan'." *New York History, New York State Historical Association*, 1 October 2010, repository.si.edu/bitstream/handle/10088/16790/anth_Manhattan. pdf?sequence=1/. Accessed 3 August 2019.

Timeless Series:
Manhattan

Michael Peter

24 photographs

24 drawings

1515 Broadway – George Abbott Way

The 1515 Broadway, also known as One Astor Plaza, is considered the 50th tallest buildings in New York City. Built on the site of the former Hotel Astor, it was designed by one of the great New York architects of the 20th Century.[1]

History awaits right on the corner with a section of West 45th Street named for Broadway producer and director George Abbott (1887-1995). George Abbott changed the American theater in many ways.[2]

---

1   Wikipedia contributors. "One Astor Plaza." *Wikipedia, The Free Encyclopedia*, 16 February 2006, en.wikipedia.org/w/index.php?title=One_Astor_Plaza&oldid=903438084. Accessed 25 June 2019.

2   Griffith, Shirley and Ember, Steve. "People in America – George Abbott, 1887-1995: He Was Known as 'Mr. Broadway'." *Voice of America*, 26 November 2005, www.manythings.org/voa/people/George_Abbott.html. Accessed 25 June 2019.

186 Fifth Avenue

The landmarked warm red brick building showing the New York City distinctive fire escape staircases, faces the famous Flatiron Building. The 186 Fifth Avenue was originally constructed for the Western Union Telegraph Company founded in 1851 which had the largest telegraph system ever established.[1]

Behind an eye-catching culmination of lower Fifth Avenue is the 1898 Sohmer Piano Co. Building at 170 Fifth Avenue, with its ribbed gold dome. This distinguished Neo-Classical building was designed for the real estate developer Henry Corn in 1897 who was responsible for the transformation of lower Fifth Avenue from 14th Street to 23rd Street.[2]

1   Hay, Alexandra. "Don't Forget to Look Up: Fifth Avenue from Washington Square to 34th Street." *Untapped Cities*, 6 September 2013, untappedcities.com/2013/09/06/dont-forget-to-look-up-fifth-avenue-washington-square-to-34th-street/. Accessed 25 June 2019.

2   Miller, Tom. "The stories behind the buildings, statues and other points of interest that make Manhattan fascinating. – The 1898 Sohmer Piano Co. Building – 170 Fifth Avenue." *Daytonian in Manhattan*, 27 June 2011, daytoninmanhattan.blogspot.com/2011/06/1898-sohmer-piano-co-building-170-fifth.html. Accessed 25 June 2019.

Grand Hyatt New York, 109 E. 42nd Street

The Grand Hyatt New York, adjacent to one of New York City's most iconic and fascinating landmarks, the Grand Central Terminal,[1] was formerly named Commodore Hotel, in honor of "Commodore" Cornelius Vanderbilt, originator of the New York Central Railroad System[2] and who had the beautiful Beaux-Arts station built; the Grand Central Terminal, unveiled in 1913, was reflecting the neighborhood's growth.[3]

Significant new improvements are planned to transform the Grand Hyatt New York to bring, amongst other things, a new icon to the New York's skyline.[4]

1   Itzkowitz, Laura. "Secrets of New York City's Grand Central Terminal", *HuffPost*, 5 January 2016, www.huffpost.com/entry/secrets-of-new-york-citys_b_8916528. Accessed 25 June 2019.

2   Truman, Jamie. "The Grand Hyatt Hotel – Historic Sites, Monuments, Landmarks, and Public Art." *Clio*, 18 April 2018, www.theclio.com/web/entry?id=58830. Accessed 25 June 2019.

3   "NY Transit Museum – Grand By Design: A History of Grand Central Terminal Making Midtown Into Mid Town", *Grand Central Terminal*, 10 February 2014, www.grandcentralterminal.com/history/. Accessed 25 June 2019.

4   Bell, Diana. "TF Cornerstone, MSD Partners Jump Into NY's Midtown East Rezoning Boom in Revamping Grand Hyatt Hotel – Plans Call for Doubling Property's Size With Added Office, Retail Space." *CoStar*, 13 February 2019, product.costar.com/home/news/shared/1122339151. Accessed 25 June 2019.

At the Pinnacle of Times Square

The ads in Times Square are known as an attraction for the 100 million of tourists who visit New York City each year.[1]

Dazzling from any perspective, the American Eagle Outfitters 12-faceted billboard plays animations 18 hours a day.[2] It is located directly across from Father Duffy Square, allowing for pedestrians to sit and relax while viewing brand messages.[3] The distinctive exterior architecture represents a new achievement in technical and artistic outdoor LED displays and in creating a dominant visual landmark.[4]

1   Archer, Seth. "Here are some mind-blowing facts about the ads in Times Square." *Business Insider*, 14 June 2016, www.businessinsider.com/surprising-facts-about-size-of-times-square-ads-2016-6. Accessed 25 June 2019.

2   Griner, David. "10 Cool Uses of American Eagle's Stunning Times Square LED Sign." *Adweek*, 1 August 2011, www.adweek.com/creativity/10-cool-uses-american-eagles-stunning-led-sign-times-square-133790/. Accessed 25 June 2019.

3   "Digital Screens & Billboards – American Eagle Times Square." *Times Square the Official Website, Times Square District Management Association, Inc.*, 25 October 2011, www.timessquarenyc.org/do-business/promote-partner/advertising-sponsorships/digital-screens-billboards. Accessed 25 June 2019.

4   "Press Release – Barco and the Barnycz Group Partner with American Eagle Outfitters on Times Square LED Display." *Barco*, 10 March 2010, www.barco.com/en/News/Press-releases/Barco-and-the-Barnycz-Group-Partner-with-American-Eagle-Outfitters-on-Times-Square-LED-Display.aspx. Accessed 25 June 2019.

Midtown South – Fifth Avenue

Fifth Avenue's quintessence began in 1811 with a much more functional name: Middle Road, the only road to provide access to this undeveloped portion of Manhattan.[1]

Built in 1907, the 366 Fifth Avenue, known as the New York Accessories Exchange Building, emerges as the heart of the fashion trade industry especially of the accessories trade.[2]

John Jacob Astor arrived from London in 1784[3] and his two sons had two grand mansions erected at 338 and 350 on what became the Fifth Avenue. Thereafter both were replaced by the original Waldorf Hotel and the Astoria Hotel. The Waldorf-Astoria Hotel was demolished in 1930 to make way for the 102-floor Art Deco masterpiece that will carry the notorious number 350: The Empire State Building.[4]

At 330 Fifth Avenue is erected the Astor Building built in 1926 for the Astor Family with the elegance of the original Colonial Revival design.[5]

Fifth Avenue is now considered the most prestigious residential district in the United States and is the traditional route for many parades.[6]

---

1   Young, Michelle. "Architecture, Features, History, Manhattan – A guide to the gilded age mansions of 5th Avenue's millionaire row." *6sqft*, 22 August 2017, www.6sqft.com/a-guide-to-the-gilded-age-mansions-of-5th-avenues-millionaire-row/. Accessed 25 June 2019.

2   "366 Fifth Avenue." *Landmark Branding LLC*, 13 July 2015, landmarkbranding.com/366-fifth-avenue/. Accessed 25 June 2019.

3   Gray, Christopher. "Streetscapes: The Office of the Astor Estate; A 'Frankly Modern' Addition." *The New York Times*, 12 January 1992, www.nytimes.com/1992/01/12/realestate/streetscapes-the-office-of-the-astor-estate-a-frankly-modern-addition.html. Accessed 25 June 2019.

4   Miller, Tom. "The stories behind the buildings, statues and other points of interest that make Manhattan fascinating. The Ultimate Family Feud - The Lost Astor Houses 5th Avenue and 34th Street." *Daytonian in Manhattan*, 27 February 2012, daytoninmanhattan.blogspot.com/2012/02/ultimate-family-feud-lost-astor-houses.html. Accessed 15 March 2020.

5   "330 Fifth Avenue, The Astor Building." *Landmark Branding LLC*, 1 June 2015, landmarkbranding.com/330-fifth-avenue-the-astor-building/. Accessed 25 June 2019.

6   Wikipedia contributors. "Fifth Avenue." *Wikipedia, The Free Encyclopedia*, 16 October 2003, en.wikipedia.org/w/index.php?title=Fifth_Avenue&oldid=896390928. Accessed 25 June 2019.

A Major Crosstown Street

The 42nd Street crosses through the island of Manhattan from Hudson River to East River.[1] Hence, it comes as no surprise that before Broadway and 42nd Street became one most famous intersection these streets were known, in 1913, for another milestone: the starting point for the nation's first transcontinental road, the Lincoln Highway.[2]

The break in New York's street grid, caused by the intersection of Broadway, allowed for designing a dynamic asymmetrical tower that responded to pedestrian traffic from the underground train station. In 2002, the National Headquarters of Ernst and Young, at 5 Times Square, became an innovative addition to the Manhattan skyline.[3]

1   Wikipedia contributors. "42nd Street (Manhattan)." *Wikipedia, The Free Encyclopedia*, 8 July 2002, en.wikipedia.org/w/index.php?title=42nd_Street_(Manhattan)&oldid=902379500. Accessed 25 June 2019.

2   "The 1913 Lincoln Highway began in Times Square." *Ephemeral New York*, 15 December 2014, ephemeralnewyork.wordpress.com/2014/12/15/the-1913-lincoln-highway-began-in-times-square/. Accessed 25 June 2019.

3   "5 Times Square – Ernst & Young National Headquarters." *Wired New York*, 1 February 2002, wirednewyork.com/skyscrapers/5-times-square/. Accessed 25 June 2019.

701 Seventh Avenue – 20 Times Square

At the epicenter of Manhattan's most hyperactive retail district,[1] is one the highest-resolution display in the history of Times Square representing over 17,000 square feet of LED display technology with more than 26.6 million pixels. Among the largest continuous exterior displays in the world,[2] the massive screen gives the feeling of sleek and fascinating futurism.[3]

Besides, behind the ads, the 701 7th Avenue was known by a variety of names during its century-long life span: Columbia Theater, Mayfair Theatre, Brandt Theatres, DeMille Theatre, Mark I-II-III and Embassy 1-2-3 Theatre.[4]

1   "Times Square's Smartest Sign." *20 Times Square*, 16 May 2014, 20timessquare.com/times-square-signage/. Accessed 26 June 2019.

2   Mutter, Zoe. "Analog Way and SNA Displays drive highest-resolution LED screen in Times Square." *AV Magazine*, 14 November 2017, www.avinteractive.com/news/analog-way-sna-displays-drive-highest-resolution-led-screen-times-square-14-11-2017/. Accessed 29 January 2020.

3   Rizzo, Cailey. "This New Times Square Hotel Will Be Wrapped in New York City's Biggest Billboard." *Travel + Leisure*, 28 November 2017, www.travelandleisure.com/hotels-resorts/hotel-openings/marriot-edition-hotel-times-square-ian-schrager. Accessed 26 June 2019.

4   Ogorodnikov, Vitali. "The Phantom of Times Square: A Century of Radical Change At 701 Seventh Avenue." *New York YIMBY*, 12 February 2016, newyorkyimby.com/2016/02/the-phantom-of-times-square-a-century-of-radical-change-at-701-seventh-avenue.html. Accessed 25 June 2020.

TriBeCa Neighborhood Lower Manhattan

Adjacent to the Ground Zero memorial is the World Trade Center Transportation Hub, the Oculus.[1] It was designed and oriented in a way that allows sunlight to cross the floor directly along the axis of the building, creating a path of light that travels through the skylight exactly on September 11th each year. It represents *"the light that continues to shine through after the darkness of the tragedy"*.[2] The Oculus symbolizes a dove released from a child's hand.[3]

In the foreground of the picture is the Underwood Building, a 18-story Neo-Classical construction completed in 1912[4] for the famous Underwood Typewriter Company.[5]

Erected in 2007, the Barclay Tower is sitting directly across the street from the great Woolworth Building and is overlooking City Hall Park.[6]

Located on the corner of Broadway and Vesey Street[7] the Transportation Building built in 1927 bears the address of 225 Broadway.[8]

1   Landrum, Susan. "NYC's Oculus: Architecture as Sculpture." *Finding NYC*, 26 August 2016, findingnyc.com/2016/08/26/oculus/. Accessed 26 June 2019.

2   Gannon, Devin. "The retractable skylight at the World Trade Center Oculus will reopen on 9/11". *6sqft*, 10 September 2018. Accessed 30 January 2020.

3   Baldwin, Eric. "World Trade Center Transportation Hub Oculus Designed in Remembrance of 9/11." *ArchDaily*, 11 September 2018, www.archdaily.com/901840/world-trade-center-transportation-hub-oculus-designed-in-remembrance-of-9-11. Accessed 26 June 2019.

4   "Underwood Building (New York City, New York)." *Wikimapia*, 26 June 2014, wikimapia.org/21917574/Underwood-Building. Accessed 26 June 2019.

5   Young, Greg and Meyers, Tom. "Tribute to a scrappy typewriter tower in lower Manhattan (yes, typewriters, remember those?)." *The Bowery Boys New York City History*, 1 June 2011, www.boweryboyshistory.com/2011/06/tribute-to-scrappy-typewriter-tower-in.html. Accessed 26 June 2019.

6   Wikipedia contributors. "Barclay Tower." *Wikipedia, The Free Encyclopedia*, 18 November 2009, en.wikipedia.org/w/index.php?title=Barclay_Tower&oldid=894126449. Accessed 26 June 2019.

7   Dunlap, David W. "Commercial Property; Former Astor Office Building Looks Back, and Up." *The New York Times*, 7 July 1999, www.nytimes.com/1999/07/07/nyregion/commercial-property-former-astor-office-building-looks-back-and-up.html. Accessed 26 June 2019.

8   Wikipedia contributors. "Transportation Building 225 Broadway." *Wikipedia, The Free Encyclopedia*, 10 June 2015, en.wikipedia.org/w/index.php?title=Transportation_Building_(Manhattan)&oldid=865399906. Accessed 26 June 2019.

At the Crossroads of the World

Broadway did not bear its current name until the late 19th century. It is the oldest North–South main thoroughfare in New York City. The Native American trail was adopted by the Dutch as their own High Street (Heere Straat). Later, the British translated it to Broad Street.[1]

As early as 1880 Broadway was illuminated by Brush arc lamps, but it is on 1902, inspired by the millions of lights on theatre marquees and billboard advertisements, that the famous nickname of "Great White Way" appeared for the first time in the New York Evening Telegram.[2]

The 4 Times Square, formerly knows as The Condé Nast Building, is the centerpiece of the 42nd Street. The building top expresses a high-technology style with 5 LED boards, one of them in 4K resolution, reflecting the flagship of H&M.[3]

One of the most glorious emblem of architectural imagery on the New York skyline, sitting at the intersection of 42nd Street and Lexington Avenue, is the Chrysler Building.[4]

1   Wikipedia contributors. "Broadway (Manhattan)." *Wikipedia, The Free Encyclopedia*, 17 April 2005, en.wikipedia.org/w/index.php?title=Broadway_(Manhattan)&oldid=900181686. Accessed 26 June 2019.

2   "Great White Way – the term." *GreatWhiteWay.com*, 6 April 2016, greatwhiteway.com/about.shtml. Accessed 25 June 2020.

3   "4 Times Square – The Conde Nast Building." *Wired New York*, 1 February 2001, wirednewyork.com/skyscrapers/4-times-square/. Accessed 26 June 2019.

4   Wikipedia contributors. "Chrysler Building." *Wikipedia, The Free Encyclopedia*, 4 January 2004, en.wikipedia.org/w/index.php?title=Chrysler_Building&oldid=903287332. Accessed 26 June 2019.

Panorama from Left to Right

The David N. Dinkins Manhattan Municipal Building was crowned in 1914 by the figure of Civic Fame to celebrate the consolidation of New York City's five boroughs. Designated New York City landmark in 1966, the 40-story building, at 1 Center Street, was the first to incorporate a subway station.[1]<> The Four Seasons Hotel New York Downtown, also known as 30 Park Place, is a 82-story completed in 2016.[2]<> The Woolworth Building, at 233 Broadway, was built in 1913 and conceived by the founder of the popular five and dimes store.[3]<> The Murry Bergtraum High School for business, at 411 Pearl Street, was one of the first business-themed high schools in New York City established in 1975.[4]<> The Intergate.Manhattan is a 32-story, at 375 Pearl Street, originally developed in 1975 for Verizon as a telecom switching hub.[5]<> The red-brick 12-building complex on Monroe Street was completed in 1933. Known as the Knickerbocker Village, it was the first federally-funded apartment complex in the United Sates.[6]<> First skyscraper of its scale to rise 847 feet into the sky of the Lower East Side, One Manhattan Square is a true vertical village built in 2019.[7]

---

1   Wikipedia contributors. "Manhattan Municipal Building." *Wikipedia, The Free Encyclopedia*, 25 June 2006, en.wikipedia.org/w/index.php?title=Manhattan_Municipal_Building&oldid=901475586. Accessed 26 June 2019.

2   Wikipedia contributors. "Four Seasons Hotel New York Downtown." *Wikipedia, The Free Encyclopedia*, 13 February 2017, en.wikipedia.org/w/index.php?title=Four_Seasons_Hotel_New_York_Downtown&oldid=903128280. Accessed 26 June 2019.

3   Wikipedia contributors. "Woolworth Building." *Wikipedia, The Free Encyclopedia*, 3 February 2004, en.wikipedia.org/w/index.php?title=Woolworth_Building&oldid=902698898. Accessed 26 June 2019.

4   Wikipedia contributors. "Murry Bergtraum High School." *Wikipedia, The Free Encyclopedia*, 6 March 2006, en.wikipedia.org/w/index.php?title=Murry_Bergtraum_High_School&oldid=900201473. Accessed 26 June 2019.

5   Miller, Rich. "Datagram Expands to Higher Ground at Intergate.Manhattan." *Data Center Knowledge*, 22 October 2013, www.datacenterknowledge.com/archives/2013/10/22/datagram-expands-to-higher-ground-at-intergate-manhattan. Accessed February 9, 2020.

6   Hughes, Carroll Joseph. "Living In - Two Bridges: Once Quiet, Now at the Edge of Change." *The New York Times*, 6 December 2017, www.nytimes.com/2017/12/06/realestate/living-in-two-bridges-lower-east-side.html. Accessed 26 June 2019.

7   "One Manhattan Square – Explore the Vertical Village." *OneManhattanSquare*, 14 April 2016, onemanhattansquare.com/. Accessed 26 June 2019.

Times Square

In 1872, carriage making was a vigorous business in the Manhattan area around 43rd Street. City officials called it Longacre Square after London's carriage district,[1] and the area had become the center of New York's horse carriage industry. It was renamed Times Square in April 1904 once the New York Times moved its headquarters to the Times Building.[2]

Times Square Studios is on the site of the former Hotel Claridge, built in 1911,[3] demolished in 1972 to make room to a 34-story skyscraper[4] housing the National Theatre which marquee was one of the largest in New York City. The 34-story building was dramatically transformed in 1985[5] and in turn the theatre was gutted to host the new studio for ABC's "Good Morning America" television show in 1999.[6] Together with its undulating corner-turning marquee features a double-ribbon ticker of news highlights, the facility, designed by Disney Imagineering, is then trailblazing the future of media-façade-based, besides to create a "looking glass".[7]

1   Sinagra, Joe. "A Short History of Longacre Square." *Save Jersey Advertising, LLC*, 31 December 2014, savejersey.com/2014/12/history-times-square-new-york/. Accessed 9 February 2020.

2   "History of Times Square. Before the American Revolution, the area that is now Times Square was rolling countryside, used for farming and breeding horses." *The Telegraph*, 27 July 2011, www.telegraph.co.uk/news/worldnews/northamerica/usa/8664743/History-of-Times-Square.html. Accessed 9 February 2020.

3   Turkel, Stanley. "Hotel Mavens: Lucius M. Boomer, George C. Boldt and Oscar of the Waldorf." Authorhouse, p.75, 19 September 2014.

4   Wikipedia contributors. "Times Square Studios." *Wikipedia, The Free Encyclopedia*, 13 September 2006, en.wikipedia.org/w/index.php?title=Times_Square_Studios&oldid=903601153. Accessed 27 June 2019.

5   "1500 Broadway (New York City, New York)." *Wikimapia* , 28 December 2016, wikimapia.org/608359/1500-Broadway. Accessed 9 February 2020.

6   Savage, Jamal. "National Twin." *Cinema Treasures*, 19 June 2012, cinematreasures.org/theaters/1853. Accessed 9 February 2020.

7   Carter, Bill. "Part ABC Studio, Part Disney Billboard." *The New York Times*, 18 September 1999, www.nytimes.com/1999/09/18/business/part-abc-studio-part-disney-billboard.html. Accessed 27 June 2019.

285 Fulton Street

At 285 Fulton Street, One World Trade Center stands with a shifting canvas of clouds and sky on its reflective glass walls like a moving work of art. The bold elegance of the new icon of New York skyline reaches 1,776 feet high, symbolizing the year the U.S. declared its independence.[1]

Fulton Street is a busy street located in Lower Manhattan in the Financial District, named in honor of Robert Fulton, an engineer who became famous for his invention of the steamship in 1809.[2]

195 Broadway is a landmarked office building in the Financial District of the borough of Manhattan. Built in 1916, the 29-story with Doric columns was the headquarters of American Telephone and Telegraph Company (AT&T) for over 70 years[3] and the site of the world's first transatlantic phone call made to London on January 7, 1927.[4]

---

1   Kamin, Blair. "One World Trade Center 'a bold but flawed giant'." *Chicago Tribune*, 18 October 2014, www.chicagotribune.com/columns/ct-one-world-trade-center-review-kamin-met-1019-20141017-column.html. Accessed 27 June 2019.

2   FNY contributors. "Fulton Street, Manhattan." *Forgotten New York*, 11 May 2003, forgotten-ny. com/2003/05/fulton-street-manhattan/. Accessed 27 June 2019.

3   Fletcher, Tom. "American Telephone and Telegraph Building." *NYC-Architecture*, New York Architecture, 29 May 2004, www.nyc-architecture.com/LM/LM069.htm. Accessed 27 June 2019.

4   "Telephone Building and a Golden Boy." *Big Apple Secrets. Hidden treasures of New York*, 22 January 2019, www.bigapplesecrets.com/2019/01/telephone-building-and-golden-boy.html. Accessed 27 June 2019.

The Thomson Reuters Building

In the 1850s, Baron Paul Julius de Reuter formed a media empire using a combination of technologies and his telegraph expertise.[1] In 1865, Reuters was the first to provide the news of the assassination of U.S. President Abraham Lincoln hours before its competitors.[2] Reuters had become one of the world's major news agencies, supplying both text and images to newspapers, other news agencies, radio and television broadcasters.

The Thomson Reuters Building is adjacent to the 1 Times Square and the Paramount Building, with a large curving glass wall facing the corner of 42nd Street and Seventh Avenue.[3]

(The reflection in the curving glass wall of the Reuters Building is of One Times Square building and The Condé Nast Building.)

---

1   The Editors of Encyclopaedia Britannica. "Paul Julius, baron von Reuter, German Journalist." *Encyclopaedia Britannica*, 15 September 2015, www.britannica.com/biography/Paul-Julius-Freiherr-von-Reuter. Accessed 27 June 2019.

2   The Editors of Encyclopaedia Britannica. "Thomson Reuters Canadian Company." *Encyclopaedia Britannica*, 27 September 2018, www.britannica.com/topic/Thomson-Reuters. Accessed 27 June 2019.

3   Giovannini, Joseph. "Acing the Deuce. Fox & Fowle transformed 42nd Street by defying convention with exuberant Times Square towers for Condé Nast and Reuters." *NYC-Architecture, New York Architecture*, 15 July 2000, www.nyc-architecture.com/MID/MID106.htm. Accessed 23 February 2020.

Newspaper Publishing Center (1830-1920)

Nassau Street, named after William of Nassau who became King William III of England, once housed many newspapers.[1] At the corner of Nassau and Spruce streets, the 1896 Beaux-Arts Building known for its outstanding architectural details was erected by the American Tract Society, a nonprofit publishing organization.[2]

The Morse Building (of Morse code fame) dating to 1878[3] was built by the nephews of Samuel F. B. Morse whose early experiments with the telegraph were conducted on this site.[4] It was designated a New York City landmark in September 2006.

Built by the Liberty-Nassau Building Company, the Liberty Tower was known as the Bryant Building for William Cullen Bryant, editor of the New York Evening Post.[5] The slender tower at 55 Liberty owes its charm to its unusual Gothic style and its white terracotta cladding.[6] The building was designated a City landmark in 1982.

Formerly known as the Marine Midland Building and HSBC Bank Building, the building was completed in 1968 and designated a New York City landmark under the name "140 Broadway" in 2013. The 51 story tower's fenestration is an eye-catching iconic building.[7]

---

1   Wikipedia contributors. "Nassau Street (Manhattan)." *Wikipedia, The Free Encyclopedia*, 26 September 2007, en.wikipedia.org/w/index.php?title=Nassau_Street_(Manhattan)&oldid=771027965. Accessed 27 June 2019.

2   Nielsen, Henrik. "150 Nassau Street, New York City, NY." *Condopedia*, 24 October 2013, www.condopedia.com/w/index.php?title=150_Nassau_Street&oldid=53519. Accessed 27 June 2019.

3   Rothbloom, Richard. "Building: Liberty Tower, 55 Liberty Street, New York, NY, 10005." *StreetEasy, Zillow Group*, 30 March 2014, streeteasy.com/building/liberty-tower. Accessed 27 June 2019.

4   Wikipedia contributors. "Morse Building." *Wikipedia, The Free Encyclopedia*, 20 March 2017, en.wikipedia.org/w/index.php?title=Morse_Building&oldid=882415428. Accessed 27 June 2019.

5   Grant, Kenneth. "Liberty Tower." *NewYorkitecture*, 22 February 2015, www.newyorkitecture.com/liberty-tower/. Accessed 27 June 2019.

6   Latchinova, Lydia and Robins, Anthony W.. "Liberty Tower, 55 Liberty Street, Borough of Manhattan. Built 1909-10; architect Henry Ives Cobb. Designation List 158 LP-1243." *Neighborhood Preservation Center, New York City Landmarks Preservation Commission*, 24 August 1982, neighborhoodpreservationcenter.org/db/bb_files/82---LIBERTY-TOWER.pdf. Accessed 27 June 2019.

7   "140broadway.com/The-building." *One|Forthy Broadway, Union Investment*, 23 July 2016, www.140broadway.com/The-building.html. Accessed 27 June 2019.

The Glitz of Times Square

A statue of George M. Cohan commemorates the first coast-to-coast superstar. He was a successful actor, singer, dancer, playwright, composer, librettist, producer and director, known as "The Man Who Owned Broadway" and considered the father of American musical comedy.[1]

Paramount Pictures built its headquarters at 1501 Broadway. The iconic landmarked tower today marrying the Golden Age of Hollywood with the 21st Century contemporary designs is known for its large four-faced clock topped by an ornamental glass globe.[2] The hours indicated by five-pointed stars are forming a circle of stars as used in the Paramount Pictures logo.[3]

One Times Square is famous for the annual New Year's Eve ball dropping ceremony. In 1904, The New York Times' owner, Adolph Simon Ochs, welcomed in the New Year with fireworks that transformed One Times Square into "a torch to usher in the new born, funeral pyre for the old which pierced the very heavens".[4] Since 2000, the One Times Square's ball is made of Waterford Crystal and LEDs and the iconic setting for the annual New Year's Eve ball dropping ceremony is completely computer controlled.[5]

1   Mayne, Marcia. "Ever Notice These Statues in Times Square?" *Inside Journeys*, 17 December 2011, insidejourneys.com/notice-statues-times-square/. Accessed 27 June 2019.

2   "History Redefined in Midtown Manhattan." *Paramount Building*, 7 November 2017, www.paramountbuilding.com/history. Accessed 27 June 2019.

3   Wikipedia contributors. "1501 Broadway." *Wikipedia, The Free Encyclopedia*, 5 May 2011, en.wikipedia.org/w/index.php?title=1501_Broadway&oldid=869192273. Accessed 27 June 2019.

4   Keyser, Hannah. "The Story Behind Times Square's New Year's Eve Celebration." *Mental Floss*, 31 December 2014, mentalfloss.com/article/60828/story-behind-times-squares-new-years-eve-celebration. Accessed 27 June 2019.

5   "Times Square History." *NYCTourist*, 29 August 2008, www.nyctourist.com/times-square-history.php. Accessed 27 June 2019.

Lafayette Street

Located at 87 Lafayette Street in the Civic Center neighborhood of Manhattan, the Firehouse Engine Company 31 is a historic fire station that was built in 1895 in the style of chateau in the Loire Valley of France.[1] The building was designated a New York City Landmark in 1966 and added to the National Register of Historic Places in 1972.[2]

Lafayette Street is named after the French hero of the American Revolutionary War, Gilbert du Motier, Marquis de Lafayette.[3]

1   Wikipedia contributors. "Firehouse, Engine Company 31." *Wikipedia, The Free Encyclopedia*, 3 June 2016, en.wikipedia.org/w/index.php?title=Firehouse,_Engine_Company_31&oldid=866328010. Accessed 27 June 2019.

2   Grant, Kenneth. "Engine Company 31." *NewYorkitecture*, 22 February 2015, www.newyorkitecture.com/engine-company-31/. Accessed 27 June 2019.

3   FNY contributors. "Lafayette Street, NoHo." *Forgotten New York*, 27 March 2013, forgotten-ny.com/2013/03/lafayette-street-noho/. Accessed 27 June 2019.

The Hearst Tower

Stretching a full block along the west side of Eighth Avenue between 56th and 57th Streets, the Hearst Tower actually occupies the shell of the original Hearst Magazine building a six-story completed in 1928,[1] commissioned by William Randolph Hearst, the media myth-maker who owned several magazines.[2] It was designated as a Landmark Site by the Landmarks Preservation Commission in 1988.[3]

The world headquarters of Hearst Communications, a 46-story structure opened in 2006, rises nearly 600 feet above its landmark six-story base.[4] Its innovative glass and steel diagrid facade has the uncommon triangular framing pattern creating a distinctive faceted silhouette on the New York skyline.[5]

1   Adams, Janet. "Hearst Magazine Building, 951-69 Eighth Avenue/301-13 West 56th Street/302-12 West 57th street, Borough of Manhattan. Built 1927-28; architects: Joseph Urban and George B. Post & Sons. Designation List 200 LP-1625." *Neighborhood Preservation Center, New York City Landmarks Preservation Commission*, 16 February 1988, s-media.nyc.gov/agencies/lpc/lp/1625.pdf. Accessed 27 June 2019.

2   Greenslade, Roy. "Review: The Chief: The Life of William Randolph Hearts by David Nasaw." *The Guardian*, Guardian News and Media, 3 May 2002, www.theguardian.com/books/2002/may/04/biography. Accessed 26 June 2020.

3   "Hearst Tower." *The Skyscraper Center, Council on Tall Buildings and Urban Habitat*, 27 March 2015, www.skyscrapercenter.com/building/hearst-tower/2245. Accessed 27 June 2019.

4   "Hearst Tower." *Hearst, Hearst Tower NYC*, 7 February 2014, https://www.hearst.com/real-estate/hearst-tower. Accessed 26 June 2020.

5   "The Hearst Tower, New York." *Design Build Network, Verdict Media Limited*, 15 October 2006, www.designbuild-network.com/projects/hearst/. Accessed 27 June 2019.

The Northern Triangle of Times Square

The Duffy Square is named in the honor of Father Francis Patrick Duffy, a Canadian American soldier, Roman Catholic priest and a military chaplain who served during the Spanish-American War and the World War I. Putting himself into the thick of battle to minister to the injured and dying, his presence on the battlefield was inspirational.[1]

The red steps behind the statue of Father Duffy are the roof of the theater tickets booth TKTS.[2]

Built in 1989, The Crowne Plaza Hotel is a 480-foot skyscraper hotel building.[3] The Hershey's signage integration with the Crowne Plaza Hotel represents the entire history of sign making with each of the signs representing just about every form of sign making since the 1900s. The Hershey store and its 15-story billboard incorporate the nineteen chocolate brands merchandised by the company.[4]

1   Demers, Daniel J.." WWI's 'Fighting Chaplain' Wielded Prayer." *Civil War. Association of the United States Army*, 8 March 2017, www.civilwar.com/news/recent-postings-54491/277968-wwi-s-fighting-chaplain-wielded-prayer.html. Accessed 28 June 2019.

2   Wikipedia contributors. "Duffy Square." *Wikipedia, The Free Encyclopedia*, 14 April 2009, en.wikipedia.org/w/index.php?title=Duffy_Square&oldid=896140853. Accessed 28 June 2019.

3   "Crowne Plaza Hotel." *TRData, The Real Deal, New York Real Estate News*, 11 February 2017, therealdeal.com/new-research/topics/property/crowne-plaza-hotel/. Accessed 28 June 2019.

4   Brill, Louis M.. "Hershey's How Sweet It Is: The Eye-Candy of Times Square." *SignIndustry.com*, 15 April 2008, www.signindustry.com/neon/articles/2008-04-15-LB-Hersheys_How_Sweet_it_Is_Signage_Spectacular_Times_Square.php3. Accessed 28 June 2019.

Madame Tussauds, 234 W 42nd Street

Anna Maria "Marie" Tussaud was a French artist known for her wax sculptures. The wax museum she founded in London has grown to become one of the major tourist attractions and expanded with franchises around the world.[1]

However, all started unfortunately by the death of her father killed in the Seven Years' War. Then when she was six years old, her mother moved into the home of doctor Philippe Curtius; Curtius was not only a physician but also skilled at wax modeling. He became the father figure for Marie. When Curtius died in 1794, he left his collection of waxworks to Marie. One year later, she married Francois Tussaud, and her later success in the waxworks business made the name "Tussaud" the most famous one in that form of art.[2]

1   "200 Years of Extraordinary History." *Madame Tussauds New York, Merlin Entertainment Group plc.*, 15 April 2011, www.madametussauds.com/new-york/en/about-us/our-story/. Accessed 28 June 2019.

2   Shank, Ian. "The Grisly Origins of Madame Tussaud's Wax Empire." *Artsy*, 8 Mars 2018, www.artsy.net/article/artsy-editorial-grisly-origins-madame-tussauds-wax-empire. Accessed 15 March 2020.

Greenwich Village Historic District

First Presbyterian Church, the Church of Patriots, First Church and Old First, refer to the same English inspired Gothic Revival brownstone building modeled on the Church of St. Saviour at Bath (England) and the crenellated central entrance tower on the Magdalen tower at Oxford.[1] It has been a landmark both architecturally and intellectually since its origins on Wall Street in 1716 with a rich tradition and reputation for progressive thought and action.[2]

1   Fletcher, Tom. "First Presbyterian Church." *NYC-Architecture, New York Architecture*, 22 April 2004, www.nyc-architecture.com/GV/GV004FirstPresbyterianChurch.htm. Accessed 28 June 2019.

2   Medina, Miriam. "First Church: Presbyterian." *The History Box*, 22 May 2012, www.thehistorybox.com/ny_city/nycity_worship_first_church_presbyterian_article00556.htm. Accessed 28 June 2019.

3 Times Square

Located on 7th Avenue between 42nd Street and 43rd Street, the 32-story tower is unique for its design, location and one-of-a-kind spire that serves as a communication antenna. It has numerous large electronic advertising displays across multiple facades and features one of the largest and most visible screen signs in all of the center of Midtown's business crossroads,[1] with 11 uniquely-sized, high definition LED screens, and state-of-the-art technology capable of full-motion video, simulcast events, mobile interactivity and social media integration. In addition, this iconic display lies directly adjacent to 7 Times Square, home of the famous New Year's Eve Ball.[2]

1   "About 3 Times Square." *3xsq*, Rudin Management Company Inc., 22 October 2017, www.3xsq.info/main.cfm?sid=introduction&pid=aboutprop. Accessed 27 June 2019.

2   "New York, Times Square, Thomson Reuters, Destination Description." *Branded Cities*, 23 December 2018, brandedcities.com/wp-assets/photosheets/ny/ny_tr_ps.pdf. Accessed 26 June 2020.

6 Times Square

After sixty-one years, the small iconic building on West 43rd Street with the big New York City Police Department sign has undergone renovations, becoming a real welcoming center for tourists in the "Crossroads of the World".[1]

The Knickerbocker Hotel built in 1906 and constructed of red brick with terracotta details and a prominent mansard roof in the Beaux-Arts style, was a centerpiece of Times Square throughout the Gilded Age. The building was placed on the National Register of Historic Places in 1980 and designated a New York City Landmark in 1988.[2] In the history of the Knickerbocker, the hotel bartender, Martini di Arma di Taggia, is said to have brought the martini into the world in 1912.[3]

1   "About NYPD – Mission Page." *NYC New York City Police Department*, 28 January 2017, www1.nyc.gov/site/nypd/about/about-nypd/mission.page. Accessed 27 June 2019.

2   Spencer, Luke J.. "The Secret Entrance to the Knickerbocker Hotel – An unassuming secret door once led to a legendary watering hole." *Atlas Obscura*, 30 August 2018, www.atlasobscura.com/places/the-secret-entrance-to-the-knickerbocker-hotel-new-york-new-york. Accessed 27 June 2019.

3   Jacobs, Sarah. "This Hotel Bar Claims to Have Invented the Martini – Look Inside." *Business Insider*, Business Insider, 31 May 2017, www.businessinsider.com/hotel-where-the-martini-originated-2017-5. Accessed 26 June 2020.

The Morgan Stanley Building

North of Duffy Square, originally known as Solomon Equities Building built in 1990, is the Morgan Stanley Building.[1] Seeing the 42-story building from different vantage points makes you perceive it differently. One of the setbacks, at the sixth floor, bows out in a graceful curve that is not only handsome in itself, but is also the key element in the deft shift of the building's visual axis.[2]

Morgan Stanley modified the signage to include a continuous ticker-tape band of stock quotes and vertical blade signs that merge to form a single image as one approaches the building down Broadway.[3]

1   Wikipedia contributors. "Morgan Stanley Building." *Wikipedia, The Free Encyclopedia*, 11 April 2012, en.wikipedia.org/w/index.php?title=Morgan_Stanley_Building&oldid=892021898. Accessed 28 June 2019.

2   Goldberger, Paul. "Architecture View; In Times Square, Dignity by Day, Glitter by Night." *The New York Times*, 10 February 1991, www.nytimes.com/1991/02/10/arts/architecture-view-in-times-square-dignity-by-day-glitter-by-night.html. Accessed 26 June 2020.

3   "1585 Broadway, Office Tower on Times Square." *Donnally Architects PLLC*, 2 October 2018, donnallyarchitects.com/project/1585-broadway/. Accessed 28 June 2019.

The Paramount Building

The Paramount Theatre opened in 1926. It began hosting live music along with its feature films as the swing era got underway. The Paramount was the site of the world premiere of Elvis Presley's first movie, "Love Me Tender". After years of showing movies and shows, the Paramount Theatre was closed on February 21, 1966 with the James Bond movie "Thunderball".[1] The auditorium was destroyed and today the Paramount Building is occupied in part by the Hard Rock Cafe.[2]

Hard Rock Cafe Inc. is a chain of theme restaurants founded in London. The cafe boasts a unique outdoor space above the building's historic marquee which is still home to Paramount Pictures offices and remains a Times Square landmark.[3]

1   "History Redefined in Midtown Manhattan." *Paramount Building*, 7 November 2017, www.paramountbuilding.com/history. Accessed 28 June 2019.

2   Gabel, William. "Paramount Theatre, 1501 Broadway, New York, NY 10036." *Cinema Treasures*, 13 November 2011, cinematreasures.org/theaters/548. Accessed 27 June 2019.

3   Wikipedia contributors. "Hard Rock Cafe." *Wikipedia, The Free Encyclopedia*, 28 February 2004, en.wikipedia.org/w/index.php?title=Hard_Rock_Cafe&oldid=903086384. Accessed 27 June 2019.

CPSIA information can be obtained
at www.ICGtesting.com
Printed in the USA
LVHW071746250820
664082LV00021B/3003